Tess the hen was not in the pen.

Dad had a net.

Mum had a bag.

Tess ran.

Mum ran and Dad ran.

Chip did not run.

Chip got a big box.

He set the box up.

He put in a pot.

Chip got Tess in the box.

11

Dad put Tess in the pen.

Talk about the story

What did Mum use to try to catch Tess?

What did Chip do to catch Tess?

Why did Tess go under the box?

How do you help out at home?

Missing letters

Put in the missing letter to make the word.

e a o

h_n   p_n

b_g   n_t

g_t   p_t

Spot the difference

Find the five differences in the two pictures.

Tip Top

Written by Roderick Hunt
Illustrated by Nick Schon,
based on the original characters
created by Roderick Hunt and Alex Brychta

OXFORD
UNIVERSITY PRESS

Read these words

big	tin
bin	tip
wok	top
box	on

Kipper had a big box.

He put a wok on top.

Kipper put a bin on the wok.

He put a tin on the bin.

Kipper set a jug on the tin.

22

He put a pan on the jug.

23

Kipper put a mug on the pan,

It will tip!

24

and he set Ted on top.

It did tip!

Talk about the story

What's in the picture?

What are the things in the picture that have *e* and *u* in the middle of the word? Find something in the picture that has *a* in the middle of the word. Find the three things that have *u* in the middle of the word.

pan; mug, jug, mum

Spot the difference

Find the five differences in the two pictures.

Maze

Help Chip get to Tess.